# DEDICATIONS

FOR MOM & DAD,

IRV

I HEREBY DEDICATE MY HALF OF THIS MODEST VOLUME TO BOB OKSNER.

M. KAZALEH

# ACKNOWLEDGMENTS

I'm incredulously lucky. I got my first job in comics when editor Fabian Nicieza, let me write MIGHTY MOUSE #10. And to my even greater fortune he teamed me up with artist-slash-genius, Mike Kazaleh! Something must've clicked because a year later all three of us were back as a team working on THE REN & STIMPY SHOW #1. From a mouse to a cat n' dog team. We didn't know if we had a hit or not, but we did know that we were definitely moving up the food chain.

It's now almost a year after *that,* and fan reaction has given this comic the momentum of a runaway train! Bear in mind that I fully realize that this "locomotion" continues because lots of hands besides Fabian's, Mike's, and mine are stoking the furnace. People like — Carlos Lopez, Ed Lazellari, Brad K. Joyce, Evan Skolnick, Susan Lopusniak, Will McRobb, Tom DeFalco, and Pete Tirella. Extra-special thanks go out to Cindy Emmert, Angelo Sirico, Suzanne Gaffney, and Christine Slusarz for their help keeping this trade paperback from flying off the tracks!

— Dan

THE REN & STIMPY SHOW™ PICK OF THE LITTER. Originally published in magazine form as the Ren & Stimpy Show #'s 1-4. Published by MARVEL COMICS. OFFICE OF PUBLICATION: 387 PARK AVENUE SOUTH, NEW YORK, N.Y. 10016. THE REN & STIMPY SHOW (including all prominent characters featured in this issue and the distinctive likenesses thereof) is a trademark owned and licensed for use by NICKELODEON, a programming service of Viacom International, Inc., and is used only with permission. All Ren & Stimpy material Copyright © 1993 Nickelodeon. All rights reserved.
ISBN #0-87135-970-7. First Printing July, 1993. GST #R127032852

10  9  8  7  6  5  4  3  2  1

Chapter 1

STIMPSON J. CAT, HOW COULD YOU *THINK* SUCH A THING?!

POOF!

WHAT DO YOU NEED WITH MERE MATERIAL POSSESSIONS?

*I'LL* TELL YOU *WHAT* YOU NEED, PAL!

PAF!

YOU NEED THE *KITTY KRAPPER 5000*™!

KITTY KRAPPER 5000

RESPLENDENT WITH ITS PLUSH NAUGAHYDE LINING...

...WITH SPECIAL, SPACE-AGE DESIGNED INTERIORS,*GUARANTEED* TO ENSURE...

KITTY KRAPPER 5000

...A MAXIMUM KITTY-LITTER-TO-TOE-SQUISH-AGE RATIO!

*AUGHHHHH!*

I *MUST* HAVE IT!

ADMEET EET, MAN, DON'T EET FEEL *GOOD*?

IT FEELS LIKE A BIG ICKY MARK ON MY *SOUL!*

DANGLY THINGS

WE DEED EET, STIMPY!

WE LOOKED THE STEELY, COLD GLANCE OF OL' MAN AUTHORITY IN THE EYE AND LAUGHED!

LAUGHED, I TELL YOU!

DON'T YOU SEE WHAT THEES MEANS? *CRIME PAYS!*

STOP IT! YOU'RE TALKING *CRAZY!*

WHAT WERE WE THINKING?

WE WERE YOUNG!

WE HAD EVERY-THING GOING FOR US!

AND *WE THREW IT ALL AWAY!!!*

SNAP OUT OF EET, MAN! THAT'S NO WAY FOR YOU TO TALK! WE'RE *MASTER CRIMINALS,* NOW!

SMEK

YEAH?

YEAH! JUST YOU AND ME, KID! TOGETHER WE COULD...

# POWDERED TOAST MAN™ VS. THE KINGS OF CRIME!

AND THAT WAS THE SCENE THIS AFTERNOON AS *EVEN* OUR CITY'S *GREATEST CHAMPION* FAILED TO STOP *THE KINGS OF CRIME!*

FINK America! 555-FINK

ESCAPING THROUGH A REAR EXIT OF THE CRIME-SITE, THESE *FELONIOUS FELONS* HAVE STOLEN *ALL OF OUR CITY'S CAPITAL!*

BANK BACK DOOR

AND NOW NO ONE CAN *BUY POWDERED TOAST!*™

WE NEED YOUR HELP! IF YOU'VE SEEN OR HEARD ANY INFORMATION ABOUT THEIR WHEREABOUTS, CALL IN AT *1-800-555-FINK!*

C'MON *YOU* CAN DO IT!

ME?

YES--*YOU!* THESE DANGEROUS CRIMINALS MUST BE BROUGHT TO *JUSTICE!* AND SO THEY CAN, BUT ONLY WITH *YOUR* HELP! CALL IN. *1-800-555-FINK!*

*1-800-555-FINK!*

HI, I KNOW THE WHEREABOUTS OF STIMPSON J. CAT AND REN HOEK... 520 MAPLE AT THE CORNER OF ELM AND--

CHEEZ, MAN! *WHAT* ARE YOU *DOING?!*

ALL RIGHT IN THERE! IT'S THE FUZZ!

AHHH! WE'RE *SURROUNDED,* STIMPY! QUEEK, RUN BEFORE EET'S...

Ren Höek was sentenced to 20 years up the river. If after a trial period he shows signs of good behavior, he'll be transferred to dry land.

Stimpson J. Cat is currently serving out his time in solitary confinement for the hygienic safety of the other prisoners.

All charges against the KITTY KRAPPER 5000™ were dropped. It now resides in Waco, Texas with its wife and family.

Chapter

2

CANADIAN LOGGING COUNTRY—WHERE MEN ARE MEN, WOMEN ARE WOMEN, AND PIZZA BOYS ARE NEITHER...

CANADIAN LOGGING CO. PIZZERIA

I'M SEECK OF THEES, I TELL YOU!

I CAN'T TAKE ANYMORE OF THEES *STUPEED* MANUAL LABOR!

PAF! PAF!

WELL, *REN*, WHY NOT DO WHAT I DO—

—MAKE A GAME OUT OF IT!

THE TIME'LL JUST *FLY* BY!

LIKE PRETENDING I'M *REALLY* **SQUISHING** THE BOSS'S INTESTINAL TRACT!

YOU'VE GOT THE HANG OF IT!

SEE, I'M PLAYING "SMILING SALAMI..."

SAUCE

SINCE YOU'VE BEEN SO KIND TO ALL THE BEAVERS, I'M HERE TO GRANT YOU *ONE* WISH.

A *WISH*?

FOR *ME*?

QUEECK MAN, USE IT BEFORE WE *DIE A HORRENDOUSLY PAINFUL DEATH!!*

HMMmmm...

BUT ONLY *ONE* WISH...

HURRY!

CREEEAK

I *KNOW!*

I WISH FOR PEACE ON EARTH!

YOUR WISH IS GRANTED!

DINK!

**Daily Kretch**

SUNNY!

PRICE: 25¢

# PEACE
## DECLARED

EARTH: Yes, incredible as it seems, the world is at peace. All wars have stopped, as political leaders all over the globe have leapt off of tall buildings. George Bush was heard to say "I've caused enough trouble already," as he plummeted to the sidewalk in a spectacular... the world.

*YOU STUPEED EEDIOT!!*

SNAP

SLAP SLAP SLAP SLAP

END.

M EET *JOE.* LIKE MOST MUTTS WITH *MANGE,* HE HAS TO GET HIS *BUTT SHAVED.*

BZZZZZT BZZZZT

BARE-BUTTED AND BACK ON THE STREET, JOE *BELIEVES* HE CAN GO BACK TO HIS NORMAL OL' LIFE.

KRUD!

POOR, DEELUUDED JOE!

FOR IT'S *HERE* THAT HE LEARNS LIFE'S *HARSHEST REALITY...*

CUTE FEMALE DOGS WON'T SNIFF A BALD-BUTTED DOG'S BUTT!

BUT *DON'T WORRY* JOE, THERE'S *HOPE* FOR YOU YET...

...THANKS TO THE *FUR CLUB FOR DOGS!*

CONDEMNED BY ORDER OF Fur club for dog2.

LET'S LOOK IN ON JOE NOW, *AFTER* A FUR-TRANSPLANT...

"AT THE END OF A LONG CREEPY ROAD, AT THE TOP OF A BEEG CREEPY MOUNTAIN WAS A HUGE CREEPY CASTLE!"

" REN, THIS IS CREEPY... "

" SHUT UP! "

FOR SALE! BEST VIEW IN THE VALLEY

"EENSIDE, THE EVEEL DR. RENHÖEKENSTIEN AND HIS STUPEED ASSEESTANT, STIMPOR, CONDUCTED THEIR BEEZARRE AND UNNATURAL EXPEREEMENTS!"

ZZFEE

AHA! I DEED EET!

THEY'RE ALIVE!

ALIVE, I TELL YOU !!

ALIVE!

AND THEY CAN PLAY EENTERMURAL SPORTS!

Sea Monkeys!

"BUT, ALAS, THE BREELIANT RENHÖEKENSTIEN COULD NOT DUPLEECATE HEES EXPEREEMENTS ON THE MACRO-SCALE!

"AND EET WAS HEES GREATEST DESIRE TO BREENG TO LIFE HEES EENANEEMATE MONSTER...—

FRANKENSTIMPY!

OH, WHERE COULD I HAVE GONE WRONG?

DEEDN'T I FOLLOW ALL OF THE EENSTRUCTIONS?!

HEY, WHAT'S THEES?!

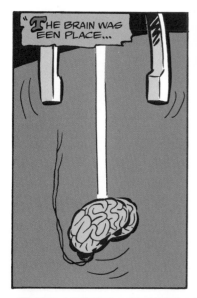

MY CREATION!
I-IT'S MOVING!

IT'S WALKING!

IT'S...IT'S...

NOW ISN'T THAT BETTER? NO MORE ICKY COBWEBS, MUCK, OR GRIME! OOH THIS PLACE WAS SUCH A MESS! NOW IF WE COULD JUST GET SOME COASTERS FOR THOSE TEST TUBES AND BEAKERS... YOU KNOW YOUR LITTLE FRIEND'S PROBABLY GOT THAT HUNCHBACK FROM BAD POSTURE, STAND UP STRAIGHT DEAR. AND I'M SURE SOME THREE-IN-ONE OIL WILL STOP THAT NASTY OL' DOOR FROM CREAKING...

...CLEANING?

I HATE HOUSEWORK !

MY CASTLE...

WHAT HAVE YOU DONE TO EET?

Chapter 3

# REN & STIMPY in ESPRESSO YOURSELF

...TO UPHOLD ALL OF THE OFFEECES OF THE PRESEEDENT OF THE U.S.A.

BUNK BA-DUNK

BADUNK BUNK BUNK BADUNK

DA PREZ

EEE GEE

THE REN & STIMPY SHOW CREATED BY John Kricfalusi

DAN SLOTT
WRITER
*
MIKE KAZALEH
ARTIST
*
BRAD K. JOYCE
LETTERER
*
ED LAZELLARI
COLORIST
*
FABIAN NICIEZA
EDITOR
*
TOM DEFALCO
EDITOR IN CHIEF

"THE" BUTTON

NOW FORK OVER THE FEDERAL RESERVES, FELLA!

OR I BLOW US ALL BACK TO THE STONE AGE!

HEH HEH

POOF!

BUNK BUNK BADUNK BUNK BUNK BADUNK

HAKKA HAKKA, JUH JUH!

STIMPY, YOU OKAY, PAL?

YOU WENT ALL FUNNY THERE FOR A SECOND.

I HAD A DREAM!

IT WAS FROM MY COLLECTIVE UNCONSCIOUS...

...DATING BACK TO THE DAWWWWWN OF TIME...

OH JOY!

THIS IS IT, REN! I NOW KNOW MY SPECIAL PURPOSE!

I UNDERSTAND WHAT I WAS PUT ON THIS EARTH TO DO!

YOU'RE SCARING ME.

AND IT'S BEA-U-TIFUL!

# Chapter 4

AND THAT'S FINAL!

≶Sigh≶

GUESS I WAS KINDA HARD ON OL' STIMPY...

STIMPY'S ROOM!

HEY MAN, I ...

WHAT'S HE UP TO ≶

-STIMPY-

OUR LIFE SAVINGS!!

BANK

HE'S GOING TO BUY A LOG™!

Stimpy's Room!

AFTER I TOLD HIM NOT TO≶

TIS' THE SEASON TO BE JOLLY!

HAPPY HAPPY HAP-HAP-PY, JOY-JOY-JOY!

EEEEEE!

REN, WHAT HAPPENED?

REN?

SNORT SNORT

?

A LOG!! ™®

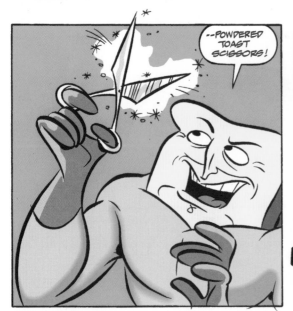